THE **TESTING** SERIES
SPEED, DISTANCE AND TIME
TESTS

THE **TESTING** SERIES
expert advice on interview preparation

Orders: Please contact How2become Ltd,
Suite 2, 50 Churchill Square Business Centre, Kings Hill, Kent ME19 4YU.
You can order via the email address info@how2become.co.uk or through
Gardners Books at Gardners.com.

First published 2011

Revised and updated 2015

ISBN: 9781910602522

Typeset for How2become Ltd by Molly Hill, Canada.

Printed in Great Britain for How2become Ltd by
Bell & Bain Ltd, 303 Burnfield Road, Thornliebank, Glasgow G46 7UQ.

CONTENTS

CHAPTER 1
WELCOME

Dear Sir/Madam,

Welcome to your new guide: *Speed, Distance and Time Tests*.

Speed, Distance and Time (SDT) questions are used during a small number of technical selection processes to assess a candidate's ability to quickly and accurately carry out often complex calculations in a short period of time.

In many cases, the assessors will require you to perform SDT questions without the use of a calculator and also without the aid of a pen and paper to write down your calculations. They will verbally fire questions at you in rapid succession in order to determine your ability to perform difficult tasks whilst under pressure. It is therefore not surprising that SDT questions are used during selection processes for jobs such as a pilot within the Armed Forces and similarly the vast majority of HM Forces Officer positions.

I recommend that you work through the examples provided within this guide before working through the large number of sample test questions. The first time you try the tests, use a pen and paper to work out your calculations. It is important that you become conversant in writing down your answers to the questions, and more importantly being able to verify how you achieved the answer. Then, get a friend or relative to sit down with you and ask you each question, only this time verbally. You will need to carry out the calculations in your head, without the aid of a pen, paper or a calculator. This is far harder to achieve and you may find your success rate drops off. However, this is fantastic practice for any SDT assessment.

One thing I need to stress from the offset is how important it is to be fully conversant and competent in the use of your 12x table. You must be able to carry out multiplication and division quickly in your head, if you are to achieve high scores in any SDT assessment. Remember, not all SDT assessments require you to carry out calculations using a pen and paper. Many of the more technical assessments will require you to perform the calculations in your head. Be prepared for every eventuality.

Whilst I do not want to insult your intelligence, here is the 12x table for you to revise and make reference to:

TIMES TABLE 12 X 12

	1	2	3	4	5	6	7	8	9	10	11	12
1	1	2	3	4	5	6	7	8	9	10	11	12
2	2	4	6	8	10	12	14	16	18	20	22	24
3	3	6	9	12	15	18	21	24	27	30	33	36
4	4	8	12	16	20	24	28	32	36	40	44	48
5	5	10	15	20	25	30	35	40	45	50	55	60
6	6	12	18	24	30	36	42	48	54	60	66	72
7	7	14	21	28	35	42	49	56	63	70	77	84
8	8	16	24	32	40	48	56	64	72	80	88	96
9	9	18	27	36	45	54	63	72	81	90	99	108
10	10	20	30	40	50	60	70	80	90	100	110	120
11	11	22	33	44	55	66	77	88	99	110	121	132
12	12	24	36	48	60	72	84	96	108	120	132	144

Finally, if you are working towards a specific career in the Armed Forces, I have created many books and DVD's on how to pass the selection processes for many different jobs, including the RAF, the Army, the Royal Navy and the Royal Marines Officer. You can find out more at:

www.how2become.com

Good luck and best wishes,

The how2become team

How2become

Disclaimer

CHAPTER 2
INTRODUCTION TO SPEED, DISTANCE & TIME

In order to be competent in the use of speed, distance and time you must aim for both accuracy and agility. By following this aim, you will achieve higher grades during the assessment in which you are undertaking. During the first part of the guide, I will provide you with a tutorial on the most effective ways to approach speed, distance and time questions. Having said that, there are alternative methods for tackling the questions, and as such, you should use these if you find them more appropriate to your style of working. During the second part of the guide I will provide you with 20 sample tests, containing a total of 400 questions.

I have already stated the importance of knowing your 12x table. I also recommend that you learn and absorb the following patterns. These will help you to answer the questions faster.

- There are 2 periods of 30 minutes in an hour
- There are 3 periods of 20 minutes in an hour
- There are 4 periods of 15 minutes in an hour

- There are 5 periods of 12 minutes in an hour
- There are 6 periods of 10 minutes in an hour
- There are 10 periods of 6 minutes in an hour
- There are 12 periods of 5 minutes in an hour
- There are 15 periods of 4 minutes in an hour
- There are 20 periods of 3 minutes in an hour
- There are 30 periods of 2 minutes in an hour
- At 60mph, you travel one mile, every minute.

When calculating speed, distance and time questions there are three variables to consider: speed, distance and time. Two of these variables will always be known.

The most effective way to solve these equations is to use the following formulas:

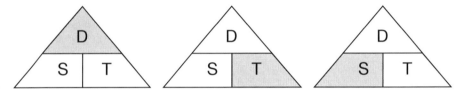

To work out the Distance:

- **Distance** = Speed x Time

To work out the Time:

- **Time** = Distance ÷ Speed

To work out the Speed:

- **Speed** = Distance ÷ Time

The triangular diagram above is a perfect aid for helping you to memorise the formula. If you place your thumb over the variable you are trying to discover, you will then see the equation required. For example, if I wanted to obtain the time, placing my thumb on T would show that I would need to divide Distance by Speed. When answering questions on speed, distance and time you may find it helpful by starting off writing down the diagram of the triangle at the top.

CALCULATING THE SPEED

CALCULATING THE SPEED

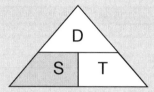

- If you are working out the speed, remember to place your thumb over the 'S' variable, and see what equation you are left with. In this case:

Speed = distance ÷ time

Method 1

What speed covers 30 miles in 2 hours and 30 minutes?

Step 1 = we know that the formula required to calculate speed = distance ÷ time.

Step 2 = first of all, we must change the time into minutes. If the question was already in minutes, then we would leave it:

2 hours 30 minutes = 150 minutes

Step 3 = speed = 30/150

Step 4 = we must now cancel down the fraction until the denominator (the bottom half of the fraction) can be multiplied into 60 (minutes).

30/150

1/5

Step 5 = we now need to multiply the denominator (the bottom part of the fraction) until it fits into 60. In this example, the outcome would be 12 (5 fits into 60, 12 times).

Step 6 = therefore the speed = 1 x 12 (5 goes into 60 twelve times) = 12 mph.

ANSWER = 12 mph.

CALCULATING THE SPEED

Method 2

What speed covers 34 miles in 10 minutes?

Step 1 = if we follow the advice in the previous method, we do not need to convert the hours into minutes, simply because it is already done for us.

Therefore, speed = distance ÷ time

Step 2 = speed = 34 ÷ 10

Step 3 = calculate how many times 10 goes into 60 minutes. Answer = 6.

    Speed = 34 x 6 (6 x 10 = 60 minutes).

ANSWER = 204 mph.

Now you try!

What speed covers 45 miles in 2 hours?

Did you work it out? Let's see if you got the correct answer!

Step 1 = speed = distance ÷ time

Step 2 = 2 hours = 120 minutes

Step 3 = 45 ÷ 2 = 22.5

ANSWER = 22.5 mph

CALCULATING THE TIME

CALCULATING THE TIME

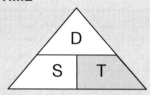

- If you are working out the time, remember to place your thumb over the 'T' variable, and see what equation you are left with. In this case:

Time = distance ÷ speed

Method 1

How long does it take to travel 48 miles at 20 mph?

Step 1 = we know that the formula for calculating time = distance ÷ speed

Time = 48/20

Step 2 = following the same process as the method used to calculate speed, the denominator needs to go into 60 (minutes). In this case, 20 will go into 60 three times:

Time = 48/20

Time = 48 x 3 (3 x 20 = 60 minutes)

Step 3 = Time = 144 minutes

Step 4 = you now need to convert the 'minutes' into 'hours and minutes'.

ANSWER = 2 hours 24 minutes

CALCULATING THE DISTANCE

CALCULATING THE DISTANCE

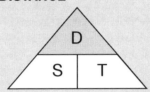

- If you are working out the distance, remember to place your thumb over the 'D' variable, and see what equation you are left with. In this case:

Distance = speed x time

Method 1

How far do you travel in 1 hour and 30 minutes at a constant speed of 40 mph?

Step 1 = we know that the formula for distance = speed x time.

Step 2 = we know that the distance = 40 x 1.5

ANSWER = 60 miles

You can also work out this type of question in your head.

Method 2

Step 1 = at 40 mph, how far do you travel in 1 hour? The answer is 40 miles.

Step 2 = At 40 mph, how far do you travel in 30 minutes? The answer is 20 miles.

Step 3 = 40 + 20 = 60 miles

ANSWER = 60 miles

FURTHER EXAMPLE QUESTIONS

Example 1

A fire engine travels 60 miles in 3 hours. What is the fire engine's speed?

Step 1 = formula = speed = distance ÷ time

Step 2 = 60 ÷ 3 = 20 mph

ANSWER = 20 mph

Example 2

A car is travelling at 30 mph for 70 minutes. What is the distance travelled?

Step 1 = with this question, it is important to remember to work in minutes. This will make it easier to carry out the calculation.

Step 2 = 30 mph = 0.5 miles per minute (30 ÷ 60)

    70 (minutes) x 0.5 = 35 miles

ANSWER = 35 miles

Example 3

A tank is driving at 48 mph over 60 miles. How long was it driving for?

Step 1 = time = distance ÷ speed

    60 ÷ 48 = 1 hour and 15 minutes

Step 2 = you know that 48 mph = 48 miles in 60 minutes.

    The difference between 60 and 48 is 12 (which is a quarter of 48).

    You can take a quarter of 60, which is 15 minutes, and add that to the 60 minutes = 75 minutes.

    75 minutes = 1 hour and 15 minutes

OR = 48 mph = 0.8 miles per minute.

    60 ÷ 0.8 = 75 minutes (1 hour and 15 minutes)

ANSWER = 1 hour and 15 minutes

FURTHER EXAMPLE QUESTIONS

Example 4

Rupert cycles at an average speed of 8 mph. If he cycles for 6 and ½ hours, how far does he travel?

Step 1 = distance = speed x time

8 x 6.5 = 52 miles

ANSWER = 52 miles

Example 5

Sally has to travel a total of 351 miles. She travels the first 216 miles in 4 hours.

   (a) Calculate her average speed for the first part of the journey.

   (b) If her average speed remains the same, calculate the total time for the complete journey.

Step 1 (a) = average speed = distance ÷ time

216 ÷ 4 = 54 mph

Step 2 (b) = time = distance ÷ speed

351 ÷ 54 = 6.5 hours

ANSWER = (a) 54 mph and (b) 6.5 hours

Example 6

Susan drives at an average speed of 45 mph on a journey of 135 miles. How long does the journey take?

Step 1 = time = distance ÷ speed

135 ÷ 45 = 3 hours

ANSWER = 3 hours

FURTHER EXAMPLE QUESTIONS

Example 7

Jermaine cycles at an average speed of 16 mph. If he cycles for 4 hours and 30 minutes, how far will Jermaine travel?

Step 1 = distance = speed x time

16 x 4.5 = 72 miles

ANSWER = 72 miles

Example 8

Becca has to travel a total of 520 miles. She travels the first 300 miles in 4 hours.

    (a) Calculate her average speed for the first part of the journey.

    (b) If her average speed remains the same, calculate the total time for the complete journey.

Step 1 (a) = average speed = distance ÷ time

        300 ÷ 4 = 75 mph

Step 2 (b) = time = distance ÷ speed

        520 ÷ 75 = 6 hours and 56 minutes

ANSWER = (a) 75 mph and (b) 6 hours and 56 minutes

CALCULATING AVERAGE SPEED, DISTANCE AND TIME

You may be asked to calculate the **overall average** speed of a journey that has multiple legs with different rates of speed.

Calculations that have more than one stage (i.e. a journey where you may have travelled by foot, car and then train) will use the same principle as the calculations shown earlier on in this chapter.

Use the speed, distance and time formula to work out each stage of the journey, but remember to add the total speeds, distances or times and divide by the number of stages, in order to calculate the overall average.

Example 1

A traveller visits three cities driving in a triangular route. He first drives from city A to B, 25 miles away, in 1 hour. He then drives from B to C, 20 miles away, in 30 minutes. Finally the traveller drives from C to A, 75 miles away, in 1 hour and 30 minutes.

Calculate the traveller's average speed.

Step 1 = work out the speed for each stage of the journey.

Stage	Distance (miles)	Time (hours)	Speed (mph)
A	25	1	25
B	20	1/2	40
C	75	1 ½	50
Total	120	3	Average speed = 40

$$\textbf{Average speed} = \frac{25 + 20 + 75}{1 + \frac{1}{2} + 1\frac{1}{2}} = \frac{120 \ miles}{3 \ hours} = 40 \ mph$$

NOTE!

If the distance data was missing from Stage B, then it could still be calculated using the speed, distance and time formula.

CALCULATING AVERAGE SPEED, DISTANCE AND TIME

Example 2

Judith drives from Plymouth to Southampton, a distance of 160 miles, in 4 hours. She then drives from Southampton to London, a distance of 90 miles, in 1 hour and 30 minutes.

Determine her average speed for each part of her journey.

Step 1 = Plymouth to Southampton average speed = 160 ÷ 4 = 40 mph

Step 2 = Southampton to London, time taken = 1 hour and 30 minutes = 1 and ½ hours or 3/2

Average speed = 90 ÷ 3/2

= 90 x 2/3

= 60 mph

Example 3

John can type 960 words in 20 minutes. Calculate his typing speed in:

(a) Words per minute;

(b) Words per hour.

Step 1 (a) = typing speed = 960 ÷ 20 = 48 words per minute

Step 2 (b) = typing speed = 48 x 60 = 2880 words per hour

Example 4

Peter drives 320 miles in 8 hours. Calculate his average speed.

Step 1 = average speed = distance ÷ time

Step 2 = 320 ÷ 8 hours = 40 mph

ANSWER = 40 mph

CALCULATING AVERAGE SPEED, DISTANCE AND TIME

Example 5

Daisy drives from Sheffield to London, a distance of 168 miles, in 4 hours.

Calculate her average speed.

Step 1 = average speed = distance ÷ time

Step 2 = 168 ÷ 4 = 42 mph

ANSWER = 42 mph

Example 6

A snail moves 8 metres in 2 hours. Calculate the average speed of the snail in metres per hour.

Step 1 = remember, the distance the snail moves is measured in metres. This means that the units used for this question will be 'meters per hour' NOT 'mph or miles per hour'.

Step 2 = 8 metres ÷ 2 = 4 metres per hour.

ANSWER = 4 metres per hour

Example 7

Javinda takes 1 and ½ hours to drive 30 km in the rush hour. Calculate his average speed in km/h.

Step 1 = remember, the distance Javinda travels is measured in kilometres. This means that the units used for this question will be in 'kilometres per hour or km/h' NOT 'mph or miles per hour'.

Step 2 = average speed = 30 km ÷ 1.5 hours = 20 km/h

ANSWER = 20 km/h

HARDER SAMPLE QUESTIONS

Example 8

An aircraft flying from London to Madrid is cruising at a speed of 534 mph. The distance from departure is 500 miles and the time remaining to reach Madrid is 1 hour 10 minutes.

What is the distance, in miles, from London to Madrid?

Step 1 = 500 miles have already been covered by the aircraft. The speed is 534 mph and the time of flight remaining is 1 hour 10 minutes = 70 minutes = 70/60 hours.

Step 2 = distance remaining = speed x time remaining

$534 \times (70 \div 60)$

623 miles.

Step 3 = therefore the distance from London to Madrid is 623 + 500 = 1,123 miles.

ANSWER = 1,123 miles

HARDER SAMPLE QUESTIONS

Example 9

On a flight from London to Rome, the following is shown on the information screen in the passenger cabin.

Current speed = 822 km/hr

Distance from departure = 1222 km

Time to destination = 22 minutes

What is the distance, in kilometres, from London to Rome?

Step 1 = 1222 km has already been covered

Distance remaining = speed x time remaining

Speed = 822 km/hr

Time = 22m = 22/60 hours

Step 2 = remaining distance = speed x time

822 x [22/60] km = 301.4 km

Step 3 = total distance between London and Rome, in km = 1222 + 301.4 = 1,523.4

ANSWER = 1,523.4 kilometres

Example 10

Given that the speed of sound in air is 340 m/s and you hear a clash of thunder 3 seconds after you see the lightning, how far away was the lightning from where you can hear the thunder?

Step 1 = sound travels at 340 m/2 from the source of the thunder. If you hear it 3 seconds later, you should use the distance = speed x time formula to calculate how far away you are from the point of thunder.

Step 2 = 340 x 3 = 1,020 metres away.

ANSWER = 1,020 metres away

HOW TO WORK THROUGH THIS GUIDE

In order to make the most out of your guide, you should quickly read through this before attempting the practice questions.

> This guide contains an array of difficulty levels, to improve your basic knowledge of speed, distance and time as well as providing the opportunity to test yourself to a more advanced level.

CALCULATOR VS. NON-CALCULATOR

Whilst some of these questions will be able to be completed without the aid of a calculator, we have also provided questions that will require you to use a calculator. This is done on **purpose**! We know that the majority of SDT assessments do not permit you to use calculators. However, we have provided these more difficult style of questions in order to engage your skills to a more advanced level. We have done this to make sure that you are fully equipped with **ANY** speed, distance and time question – no matter the difficulty level.

TIME LIMITS

Whilst we have provided time limits throughout this guide, we suggest that if you are a beginner, to practice without time limits first, until you feel confident enough to test your skills under more pressurised conditions. The time limits have been designed to create a similar impact to that of your real assessments. Generally, you will be assessed under strict time limits.

> Please note, despite the strict time limit, examiners do not expect you to finish all of the questions; they simply want to see how well you perform under pressure.
>
> Remember, it is important to work on your SPEED as well as your ACCURACY!

ROUNDING UP

For the purpose of this guide, your answers should all be rounded up to the nearest whole number. For example, 32 minutes and 33 seconds would be rounded up to 33 because there are 60 seconds in 1 minute, and '33 seconds' is over half way.

CHAPTER 3
SPEED, DISTANCE AND TIME PRACTICE TESTS

$$\text{Speed} = \frac{\text{Distance}}{\text{Time}}$$

$$\text{Distance} = \text{Speed} \times \text{Time}$$

$$\text{Time} = \frac{\text{Distance}}{\text{Speed}}$$

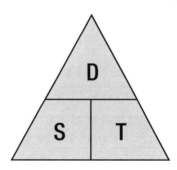

PRACTICE TEST 1

There are 20 questions and you have 5 minutes to complete the test. The answers are supplied at the end of the test.

Q1. At 4 mph, how long does it take to travel 1 mile?

ANSWER:

Q2. At 120 mph, how long does it take to travel 60 miles?

ANSWER:

Q3. At 30 mph, how far do you travel in 1 hour and 36 mins?

ANSWER:

Q4. At 1 mph, how long does it take to travel 15 miles?

ANSWER:

Q5. At 13 mph, how far can you travel in 1 hour?

ANSWER:

Q6. At 13 mph, how long does it take to travel 13 miles?

ANSWER:

Q7. At 19 mph, how long does it take to travel 19 miles?

ANSWER:

Q8. At 3 mph, how long does it take to travel 11 miles?

ANSWER:

Q9. At 60 mph, how far do you travel in 1 hour?

ANSWER:

Q10. At 36 mph, how far do you travel in 15 mins?

ANSWER:

Q11. At 90 mph, how long does it take to travel 12 miles?

ANSWER:

Q12. At 15 mph, how long does it take to travel 40 miles?

ANSWER:

Q13. What speed covers 90 miles in 2 hours?

ANSWER:

Q14. At 165 mph, how long does it take to travel 132 miles?

ANSWER:

Q15. At 21 mph, how long does it take to travel 21 miles?

ANSWER:

Q16. What speed covers 20 miles in 2 hours?

ANSWER:

Q17. At 15 mph, how long does it take to travel 88 miles?

ANSWER:

Q18. At 16 mph, how far do you travel in 3 hours?

ANSWER:

Q19. At 72 mph, how far do you travel in 25 mins?

ANSWER:

Q20. At 38 mph, how long does it take to travel 57 miles?

ANSWER:

Now check your answers with the ones that follow.

ANSWERS TO PRACTICE TEST 1

1. 15 mins

2. 30 mins

3. 48 miles

4. 15 hours

5. 13 miles

6. 1 hour

7. 1 hour

8. 3 hours and 40 mins

9. 60 miles

10. 9 miles

11. 8 mins

12. 2 hours and 40 mins

13. 45 mph

14. 48 mins

15. 1 hour

16. 10 mph

17. 5 hours and 52 mins

18. 48 miles

19. 30 miles

20. 1 hour and 30 mins

Once you are satisfied with your answers, move on to the next practice exam.

PRACTICE TEST 2

There are 20 questions and you have 5 minutes to complete the test. The answers are supplied at the end of the test.

Q1. What speed covers 19 miles in 1 hour?

ANSWER:

Q2. At 156 mph, how far do you travel in 1 hour?

ANSWER:

Q3. At 200 mph, how long does it take to travel 160 miles?

ANSWER:

Q4. What speed covers 36 miles in 1 hour?

ANSWER:

Q5. What speed covers 15 miles in 15 hours?

ANSWER:

Q6. What speed covers 3 miles in 10 mins?

ANSWER:

Q7. What speed covers 8 miles in 24 mins?

ANSWER:

Q8. At 80 mph, how long does it take to travel 140 miles?

ANSWER:

Q9. At 10 mph, how long does it take to travel 10 miles?

ANSWER:

Q10. At 170 mph, how far do you travel in 1 hour?

ANSWER:

Q11. At 20 mph, how long does it take to travel 7 miles?

ANSWER:

Q12. At 135 mph, how long does it take to travel 72 miles?

ANSWER:

Q13. What speed covers 18 miles in 10 mins?

ANSWER:

Q14. At 16 mph, how long does it take to travel 12 miles?

ANSWER:

Q15. At 2 mph, how long does it take to travel 19 miles?

ANSWER:

Q16. What speed covers 10 miles in 1 hour and 15 mins?

ANSWER:

Q17. At 16 mph, how long does it take to travel 20 miles?

ANSWER:

Q18. At 18 mph, how long does it take to travel 180 miles?

ANSWER:

Q19. What speed covers 80 miles in 4 hours?

ANSWER:

Q20. At 60 mph, how long does it take to travel 120 miles?

ANSWER:

Now check your answers with the ones that follow.

ANSWERS TO PRACTICE TEST 2

1. 19 mph
2. 156 miles
3. 48 mins
4. 36 mph
5. 1 mph
6. 18 mph
7. 20 mph
8. 1 hour and 45 mins
9. 1 hour
10. 170 miles
11. 21 mins
12. 32 mins
13. 108 mph
14. 45 mins
15. 9 hours and 30 mins
16. 8 mph
17. 1 hour and 15 mins
18. 10 hours
19. 20 mph
20. 2 hours

Once you are satisfied with your answers, move on to the next practice exam.

PRACTICE TEST 3

There are 20 questions and you have 5 minutes to complete the test. The answers are supplied at the end of the test.

Q1. At 80 mph, how far do you travel in 27 mins?

ANSWER:

Q2. What speed covers 24 miles in 2 hours and 24 mins?

ANSWER:

Q3. At 54 mph, how long does it take to travel 18 miles?

ANSWER:

Q4. What speed covers 48 miles in 15 mins?

ANSWER:

Q5. At 10 mph, how long does it take to travel 12 miles?

ANSWER:

Q6. What speed covers 45 miles in 1 hour and 40 mins?

ANSWER:

Q7. At 100 mph, how far do you travel in 18 mins?

ANSWER:

Q8. What speed covers 2 miles in 20 mins?

ANSWER:

Q9. At 44 mph, how far do you travel in 6 hours and 15 mins?

ANSWER:

Q10. At 5 mph, how long does it take to travel 7 miles?

ANSWER:

Q11. What speed covers 14 miles in 2 hours?

ANSWER:

Q12. What speed covers 15 miles in 2 hours and 30 mins?

ANSWER:

Q13. What speed covers 6 miles in 1 hour and 30 mins?

ANSWER:

Q14. What speed covers 15 miles in 45 mins?

ANSWER:

Q15. At 20 mph, how far do you travel in 3 hours and 15 mins?

ANSWER:

Q16. At 18 mph, how far do you travel in 20 mins?

ANSWER:

Q17. At 16 mph, how far do you travel in 1 hour and 15 mins?

ANSWER:

Q18. What speed covers 2 miles in 40 mins?

ANSWER:

Q19. What speed covers 8 miles in 1 hour?

ANSWER:

Q20. What speed covers 11 miles in 12 minutes?

ANSWER:

Now check your answers with the ones that follow.

ANSWERS TO PRACTICE TEST 3

1. 36 miles
2. 10 mph
3. 20 mins
4. 192 mph
5. 1 hour and 12 mins
6. 27 mph
7. 30 miles
8. 6 mph
9. 275 miles
10. 1 hour and 24 mins
11. 7 mph
12. 6 mph
13. 4 mph
14. 20 mph
15. 65 miles
16. 6 miles
17. 20 miles
18. 3 mph
19. 8 mph
20. 55 mph

Once you are satisfied with your answers, move on to the next practice exam.

PRACTICE TEST 4

There are 20 questions and you have 5 minutes to complete the test. The answers are supplied at the end of the test.

Q1. What speed covers 6 miles in 10 mins?

ANSWER:

Q2. What speed covers 25 miles in 10 mins?

ANSWER:

Q3. What speed covers 28 miles in 16 mins?

ANSWER:

Q4. At 10 mph, how far do you travel in 6 mins?

ANSWER:

Q5. What speed covers 14 miles in 1 hour and 24 mins?

ANSWER:

Q6. At 8 mph, how far do you travel in 4 hours?

ANSWER:

Q7. What speed covers 14 miles in 20 mins?

ANSWER:

Q8. At 28 mph, how long does it take to travel 84 miles?

ANSWER:

Q9. At 15 mph, how far do you travel in 1 hour and 20 mins?

ANSWER:

Q10. At 5 mph, how long does it take to travel 16 miles?

ANSWER:

Q11. What speed covers 14 miles in 2 hours?

ANSWER:

Q12. What speed covers 40 miles in 8 hours?

ANSWER:

Q13. At 18 mph, how long does it take to travel 6 miles?

ANSWER:

Q14. At 30 mph, how long does it take to travel 28 miles?

ANSWER:

Q15. What speed covers 15 miles in 3 hours?

ANSWER:

Q16. What speed covers 6 miles in 45 mins?

ANSWER:

Q17. What speed covers 4 miles in 20 mins?

ANSWER:

Q18. At 12 mph, how far do you travel in 2 hours?

ANSWER:

Q19. At 17 mph, how long does it take to travel 34 miles?

ANSWER:

Q20. What speed covers 34 miles in 24 mins?

ANSWER:

Now check your answers with the ones that follow.

ANSWERS TO PRACTICE TEST 4

1. 36 mph
2. 150 mph
3. 105 mph
4. 1 mile
5. 10 mph
6. 32 miles
7. 42 mph
8. 3 hours
9. 20 miles
10. 3 hours and 12 mins
11. 7 mph
12. 5 mph
13. 20 mins
14. 56 mins
15. 5 mph
16. 8 mph
17. 12 mph
18. 24 miles
19. 2 hours
20. 85 mph

Once you are satisfied with your answers, move on to the next practice exam.

PRACTICE TEST 5

There are 20 questions and you have 5 minutes to complete the test. The answers are supplied at the end of the test.

Q1. At 36 mph, how long does it take to travel 15 miles?

ANSWER:

Q2. What speed covers 57 miles in 9 hours and 30 mins?

ANSWER:

Q3. At 68 mph, how far do you travel in 4 hours?

ANSWER:

Q4. What speed covers 8 miles in 6 mins?

ANSWER:

Q5. At 19 mph, how long does it take to travel 76 miles?

ANSWER:

Q6. At 117 mph, how far do you travel in 1 hour and 40 mins?

ANSWER:

Q7. At 27 mph, how far do you travel in 1 hour and 20 mins?

ANSWER:

Q8. At 32 mph, how long does it take to travel 8 miles?

ANSWER:

Q9. At 6 mph, how far do you travel in 21 hours and 20 mins?

ANSWER:

Q10. At 7 mph, how far do you travel in 2 hours?

ANSWER:

Q11. What speed covers 84 miles in 36 mins?

ANSWER:

Q12. At 16 mph, how far do you travel in 6 hours and 15 mins?

ANSWER:

Q13. What speed covers 19 miles in 15 mins?

ANSWER:

Q14. At 36 mph, how long does it take to travel 120 miles?

ANSWER:

Q15. What speed covers 13 miles in 10 mins?

ANSWER:

Q16. At 9 mph, how far do you travel in 1 hour and 20 mins?

ANSWER:

Q17. What speed covers 15 miles in 12 mins?

ANSWER:

Q18. What speed covers 11 miles in 15 mins?

ANSWER:

Q19. What speed covers 14 miles in 1 hour and 10 mins?

ANSWER:

Q20. At 44 mph, how long does it take to travel 44 miles?

ANSWER:

Now check your answers with the ones that follow.

ANSWERS TO PRACTICE TEST 5

1. 25 mins
2. 6 mph
3. 272 miles
4. 80 mph
5. 4 hours
6. 195 miles
7. 36 miles
8. 15 mins
9. 128 miles
10. 14 miles
11. 140 mph
12. 100 miles
13. 76 mph
14. 3 hours and 20 mins
15. 78 mph
16. 12 miles
17. 75 mph
18. 44 mph
19. 12 mph
20. 1 hour

Once you are satisfied with your answers, move on to the next practice exam.

PRACTICE TEST 6

There are 20 questions and you have 5 minutes to complete the test. The answers are supplied at the end of the test.

Q1. What speed covers 14 miles in 2 hours and 48 mins?

ANSWER:

Q2. At 15 mph, how long does it take to travel 50 miles?

ANSWER:

Q3. What speed covers 35 miles in 6 mins?

ANSWER:

Q4. What speed covers 36 miles in 2 hours?

ANSWER:

Q5. What speed covers 18 miles in 15 mins?

ANSWER:

Q6. At 48 mph, how long does it take to travel 20 miles?

ANSWER:

Q7. What speed covers 13 miles in 15 mins?

ANSWER:

Q8. At 75 mph, how far do you travel in 1 hour and 8 mins?

ANSWER:

Q9. What speed covers 144 miles in 3 hours and 12 mins?

ANSWER:

Q10. At 20 mph, how far do you travel in 1 hour and 15 mins?

ANSWER:

Q11. What speed covers 42 miles in 2 hours?

ANSWER:

Q12. At 24 mph, how far do you travel in 3 hours and 20 mins?

ANSWER:

Q13. What speed covers 13 miles in 10 mins?

ANSWER:

Q14. At 10 mph, how far do you travel in 2 hours?

ANSWER:

Q15. At 33 mph, how long does it take to travel 55 miles?

ANSWER:

Q16. At 18 mph, how long does it take to travel 45 miles?

ANSWER:

Q17. At 15 mph, how far do you travel in 28 mins?

ANSWER:

Q18. What speed covers 350 miles in 2 hours?

ANSWER:

Q19. At 80 mph, how far do you travel in 54 mins?

ANSWER:

Q20. What speed covers 400 miles in 3 hours and 12 mins?

ANSWER:

Now check your answers with the ones that follow.

ANSWERS TO PRACTICE TEST 6

1. 5 mph
2. 3 hours and 20 mins
3. 350 mph
4. 18 mph
5. 72 mph
6. 25 mins
7. 52 mph
8. 85 miles
9. 45 mph
10. 25 miles
11. 21 mph
12. 80 miles
13. 78 mph
14. 20 miles
15. 1 hour and 40 mins
16. 2 hours and 30 mins
17. 7 miles
18. 175 mph
19. 72 miles
20. 125 mph

Once you are satisfied with your answers, move on to the next practice exam.

PRACTICE TEST 7

There are 20 questions and you have 5 minutes to complete the test. The answers are supplied at the end of the test.

Q1. What speed covers 4 miles in 15 mins?

ANSWER:

Q2. At 18 mph, how long does it take to travel 36 miles?

ANSWER:

Q3. At 30 mph, how far do you travel in 1 hour?

ANSWER:

Q4. At 26 mph, how far do you travel in 2 hours?

ANSWER:

Q5. At 24 mph, how far do you travel in 7 hours and 20 mins?

ANSWER:

Q6. At 6 mph, how long does it take to travel 15 miles?

ANSWER:

Q7. At 70 mph, how far do you travel in 1 hour and 30 mins?

ANSWER:

Q8. At 7 mph, how far do you travel in 2 hours?

ANSWER:

Q9. At 4 mph, how long does it take to travel 190 miles?

ANSWER:

Q10. What speed covers 5 miles in 5 hours?

ANSWER:

Q11. At 12 mph, how long does it take to travel 3 miles?

ANSWER:

Q12. At 15 mph, how long does it take to travel 14 miles?

ANSWER:

Q13. What speed covers 168 miles in 2 hours and 48 mins?

ANSWER:

Q14. What speed covers 7 miles in 12 mins?

ANSWER:

Q15. What speed covers 102 miles in 36 mins?

ANSWER:

Q16. At 27 mph, how long does it take to travel 18 miles?

ANSWER:

Q17. At 39 mph, how long does it take to travel 52 miles?

ANSWER:

Q18. At 171 mph, how far do you travel in 20 mins?

ANSWER:

Q19. What speed covers 52 miles in 6 hours and 30 mins?

ANSWER:

Q20. What speed covers 84 miles in 42 hours?

ANSWER:

Now check your answers with the ones that follow.

ANSWERS TO PRACTICE TEST 7

1. 16 mph
2. 2 hours
3. 30 miles
4. 52 miles
5. 176 miles
6. 2 hours and 30 mins
7. 105 miles
8. 14 miles
9. 47 hours and 30 mins
10. 1 mph
11. 15 mins
12. 56 mins
13. 60 mph
14. 35 mph
15. 170 mph
16. 40 mins
17. 1 hour and 20 mins
18. 57 miles
19. 8 mph
20. 2 mph

Once you are satisfied with your answers, move on to the next practice exam.

PRACTICE TEST 8

There are 20 questions and you have 5 minutes to complete the test. The answers are supplied at the end of the test.

Q1. At 17 mph, how long does it take to travel 136 miles?

ANSWER:

Q2. What speed covers 13 miles in 2 hours and 10 mins?

ANSWER:

Q3. At 16 mph, how long does it take to travel 20 miles?

ANSWER:

Q4. At 3 mph, how far do you travel in 2 hours and 40 mins?

ANSWER:

Q5. What speed covers 40 miles in 1 hour and 15 mins?

ANSWER:

Q6. What speed covers 80 miles in 1 hour and 20 mins?

ANSWER:

Q7. At 12 mph, how far do you travel in 15 mins?

ANSWER:

Q8. At 40 mph, how long does it take to travel 24 miles?

ANSWER:

Q9. At 20 mph, how far do you travel in 18 mins?

ANSWER:

Q10. At 57 mph, how long does it take to travel 19 miles?

ANSWER:

11. What speed covers 18 miles in 20 mins?

ANSWER:

12. What speed covers 4 miles in 16 mins?

ANSWER:

13. At 8 mph, how long does it take to travel 12 miles?

ANSWER:

14. At 20 mph, how far do you travel in 2 hours and 24 mins?

ANSWER:

Q15. At 2 mph, how far do you travel in 9 hours?

ANSWER:

Q16. At 25 mph, how far do you travel in 24 mins?

ANSWER:

Q17. At 17 mph, how long does it take to travel 68 miles?

ANSWER:

Q18. At 80 mph, how far do you travel in 1 hour and 3 mins?

ANSWER:

Q19. At 11 mph, how far do you travel in 1 hour?

ANSWER:

Q20. At 14 mph, how long does it take to travel 7 miles?

ANSWER:

Now check your answers with the ones that follow.

ANSWERS TO PRACTICE TEST 8

1. 8 hours
2. 6 mph
3. 1 hour and 15 mins
4. 8 miles
5. 32 mph
6. 60 mph
7. 3 miles
8. 36 mins
9. 6 miles
10. 20 mins
11. 54 mph
12. 15 mph
13. 1 hour and 30 mins
14. 48 miles
15. 18 miles
16. 10 miles
17. 4 hours
18. 84 miles
19. 11 miles
20. 30 mins

Once you are satisfied with your answers, move on to the next practice exam.

PRACTICE TEST 9

There are 20 questions and you have 5 minutes to complete the test. The answers are supplied at the end of the test.

Q1. At 28 mph, how far do you travel in 30 minutes?

ANSWER:

Q2. At 8 mph, how long does it take to travel 20 miles?

ANSWER:

Q3. What speed covers 10 miles in 50 mins?

ANSWER:

Q4. At 3 mph, how long does it take to travel 8 miles?

ANSWER:

Q5. At 6 mph, how long does it take to travel 16 miles?

ANSWER:

Q6. At 12 mph, how long does it take to travel 45 miles?

ANSWER:

Q7. What speed covers 135 miles in 1 hour and 15 mins?

ANSWER:

Q8. At 12 mph, how long does it take to travel 2 miles?

ANSWER:

Q9. What speed covers 42 miles in 3 hours?

ANSWER:

Q10. What speed covers 110 miles in 3 hours and 20 mins?

ANSWER:

Q11. At 100 mph, how far do you travel in 48 mins?

ANSWER:

Q12. At 10 mph, how far do you travel in 3 hours and 36 mins?

ANSWER:

Q13. At 5 mph, how long does it take to travel 56 miles?

ANSWER:

Q14. At 60 mph, how long does it take to travel 12 miles?

ANSWER:

Q15. At 3 mph, how long does it take to travel 10 miles?

ANSWER:

Q16. At 17 mph, how far do you travel in 8 hours?

ANSWER:

Q17. At 4 mph, how long does it take to travel 48 miles?

ANSWER:

Q18. At 8 mph, how long does it take to travel 20 miles?

ANSWER:

Q19. What speed covers 20 miles in 5 hours?

ANSWER:

Q20. What speed covers 11 miles in 5 hours and 30 mins?

ANSWER:

Now check your answers with the ones that follow.

ANSWERS TO PRACTICE TEST 9

1. 14 miles
2. 2 hours and 30 mins
3. 12 mph
4. 2 hours and 40 mins
5. 2 hours and 40 mins
6. 3 hours and 45 mins
7. 108 mph
8. 10 mins
9. 14 mph
10. 33 mph
11. 80 miles
12. 36 miles
13. 11 hours and 12 mins
14. 12 mins
15. 3 hours and 20 mins
16. 136 miles
17. 12 hours
18. 2 hours and 30 mins
19. 4 mph
20. 2 mph

Once you are satisfied with your answers, move on to the next practice exam.

PRACTICE TEST 10

There are 20 questions and you have 5 minutes to complete the test. The answers are supplied at the end of the test.

Q1. At 12 mph, how long does it take to travel 21 miles?

ANSWER:

Q2. What speed covers 57 miles in 36 mins?

ANSWER:

Q3. At 22 mph, how far do you travel in 30 mins?

ANSWER:

Q4. At 64 mph, how far do you travel in 45 mins?

ANSWER:

Q5. What speed covers 14 miles in 24 mins?

ANSWER:

Q6. At 10 mph, how long does it take to travel 50 miles?

ANSWER:

Q7. At 5 mph, how long does it take to travel 2 miles?

ANSWER:

Q8. At 80 mph, how long does it take to travel 48 miles?

ANSWER:

Q9. At 4 mph, how long does it take to travel 16 miles?

ANSWER:

 THE **TESTING** SERIES

Q10. At 2 mph, how far do you travel in 15 mins?

ANSWER:

Q11. At 3 mph, how far do you travel in 40 mins?

ANSWER:

Q12. At 16 mph, how far do you travel in 30 mins?

ANSWER:

Q13. What speed covers 9 miles in 20 mins?

ANSWER:

Q14. What speed covers 14 miles in 20 mins?

ANSWER:

Q15. What speed covers 15 miles in 50 mins?

ANSWER:

Q16. At 10 mph, how far do you travel in 48 mins?

ANSWER:

Q17. At 9 mph, how far do you travel in 1 hour and 20 mins?

ANSWER:

Q18. What speed covers 68 miles in 68 hours?

ANSWER:

Q19. At 18 mph, how long does it take to travel 3 miles?

ANSWER:

Q20. At 19 mph, how long does it take to travel 38 miles?

ANSWER:

Now check your answers with the ones that follow.

ANSWERS TO PRACTICE TEST 10

1. 1 hour and 45 mins
2. 95 mph
3. 11 miles
4. 48 miles
5. 35 mph
6. 5 hours
7. 24 mins
8. 36 mins
9. 4 hours
10. 0.5 miles
11. 2 miles
12. 8 miles
13. 27 mph
14. 42 mph
15. 18 mph
16. 8 miles
17. 12 miles
18. 1 mph
19. 10 mins
20. 2 hours

Once you are satisfied with your answers, move on to the next practice exam.

PRACTICE TEST 11

There are 20 questions and you have 5 minutes to complete the test. The answers are supplied at the end of the test.

Q1. At 9 mph, how far do you travel in 1 hour and 40 mins?

ANSWER:

Q2. At 64 mph, how far do you travel in 30 mins?

ANSWER:

Q3. What speed covers 168 miles in 6 hours?

ANSWER:

Q4. At 84 mph, how long does it take to travel 14 miles?

ANSWER:

Q5. At 20 mph, how long does it take to travel 72 miles?

ANSWER:

Q6. What speed covers 51 miles in 45 mins?

ANSWER:

Q7. At 20 mph, how long does it take to travel 95 miles?

ANSWER:

Q8. What speed covers 70 miles in 5 hours and 50 mins?

ANSWER:

Q9. At 6 mph, how long does it take to travel 60 miles?

ANSWER:

Q10. What speed covers 36 miles in 1 hour and 20 mins?

ANSWER:

Q11. What speed covers 9 miles in 30 mins?

ANSWER:

Q12. At 40 mph, how far do you travel in 1 hour and 30 mins?

ANSWER:

Q13. At 12 mph, how far do you travel in 1 hour and 15 mins?

ANSWER:

Q14. At 228 mph, how far do you travel in 30 mins?

ANSWER:

Q15. At 64 mph, how long does it take to travel 80 miles?

ANSWER:

Q16. At 9 mph, how long does it take to travel 24 miles?

ANSWER:

Q17. What speed covers 52 miles in 4 hours and 20 mins?

ANSWER:

Q18. What speed covers 20 miles in 30 mins?

ANSWER:

Q19. What speed covers 85 miles in 2 hours and 30 mins?

ANSWER:

Q20. What speed covers 8 miles in 20 mins?

ANSWER:

Now check your answers with the ones that follow.

ANSWERS TO PRACTICE TEST 11

1. 15 miles
2. 32 miles
3. 28 mph
4. 10 mins
5. 3 hours and 36 mins
6. 68 mph
7. 4 hours and 45 mins
8. 12 mph
9. 10 hours
10. 27 mph
11. 18 mph
12. 60 miles
13. 15 miles
14. 114 miles
15. 1 hour and 15 mins
16. 2 hours and 40 mins
17. 12 mph
18. 40 mph
19. 34 mph
20. 24 mph

Once you are satisfied with your answers, move on to the next practice exam.

PRACTICE TEST 12

There are 20 questions and you have 5 minutes to complete the test. The answers are supplied at the end of the test.

Q1. What speed covers 80 miles in 40 mins?

ANSWER:

Q2. At 14 mph, how far do you travel in 30 mins?

ANSWER:

Q3. At 96 mph, how far do you travel in 15 mins?

ANSWER:

Q4. At 9 mph, how far do you travel in 1 hour and 20 mins?

ANSWER:

Q5. At 20 mph, how long does it take to travel 12 miles?

ANSWER:

Q6. At 6 mph, how far do you travel in 1 hour and 20 mins?

ANSWER:

Q7. At 12 mph, how long does it take to travel 56 miles?

ANSWER:

Q8. At 72 mph, how long does it take to travel 108 miles?

ANSWER:

Q9. What speed covers 152 miles in 4 hours and 45 mins?

ANSWER:

Q10. At 12 mph, how far do you travel in 4 hours and 40 mins?

ANSWER:

Q11. At 90 mph, how far do you travel in 20 mins?

ANSWER:

Q12. What speed covers 19 miles in 10 mins?

ANSWER:

Q13. At 21 mph, how long does it take to travel 7 miles?

ANSWER:

Q14. At 8 mph, how far do you travel in 1 hour and 45 mins?

ANSWER:

Q15. What speed covers 2 miles in 24 mins?

ANSWER:

Q16. At 3 mph, how far do you travel in 2 hours and 20 mins?

ANSWER:

Q17. What speed covers 165 miles in 8 hours and 15 mins?

ANSWER:

Q18. At 12 mph, how long does it take to travel 9 miles?

ANSWER:

Q19. What speed covers 12 miles in 6 hours?

ANSWER:

Q20. At 30 mph, how far do you travel in 2 hours and 24 mins?

ANSWER:

Now check your answers with the ones that follow.

ANSWERS TO PRACTICE TEST 12

1. 120 mph
2. 7 miles
3. 24 miles
4. 12 miles
5. 36 mins
6. 8 miles
7. 4 hours and 40 mins
8. 1 hour and 30 mins
9. 32 mph
10. 56 miles
11. 30 miles
12. 114 mph
13. 20 mins
14. 14 miles
15. 5 mph
16. 7 miles
17. 20 mph
18. 45 mins
19. 2 mph
20. 72 miles

Once you are satisfied with your answers, move on to the next practice exam.

PRACTICE TEST 13

There are 20 questions and you have 5 minutes to complete the test. The answers are supplied at the end of the test.

Q1. What speed covers 340 miles in 2 hours?

ANSWER:

Q2. What speed covers 120 miles in 3 hours and 20 mins?

ANSWER:

Q3. At 28 mph, how far do you travel in 1 hour and 15 mins?

ANSWER:

Q4. At 12 mph, how long does it take to travel 11 miles?

ANSWER:

Q5. At 40 mph, how far do you travel in 1 hour and 30 mins?

ANSWER:

Q6. At 3 mph, how long does it take to travel 11 miles?

ANSWER:

Q7. What speed covers 30 miles in 10 mins?

ANSWER:

Q8. What speed covers 21 miles in 1 hour and 24 mins?

ANSWER:

Q9. At 10 mph, how far do you travel in 6 hours and 48 mins?

ANSWER:

Q10. What speed covers 48 miles in 24 mins?

ANSWER:

Q11. At 14 mph, how long does it take to travel 7 miles?

ANSWER:

Q12. What speed covers 44 miles in 4 hours and 24 mins?

ANSWER:

Q13. What speed covers 12 miles in 15 mins?

ANSWER:

Q14. At 12 mph, how long does it take to travel 18 miles?

ANSWER:

Q15. At 20 mph, how long does it take to travel 75 miles?

ANSWER:

Q16. At 30 mph, how far do you travel in 1 hour and 48 mins?

ANSWER:

Q17. What speed covers 20 miles in 1 hour and 15 mins?

ANSWER:

Q18. What speed covers 14 miles in 2 hours?

ANSWER:

Q19. At 20 mph, how far do you travel in 3 mins?

ANSWER:

Q20. At 8 mph, how far do you travel in 1 hour and 45 mins?

ANSWER:

D

S   T

Now check your answers with the ones that follow.

ANSWERS TO PRACTICE TEST 13

1. 170 mph
2. 36 mph
3. 35 miles
4. 55 mins
5. 60 miles
6. 3 hours and 40 mins
7. 180 mph
8. 15 mph
9. 68 miles
10. 120 mph
11. 30 mins
12. 10 mph
13. 48 mph
14. 1 hour and 30 mins
15. 3 hours and 45 mins
16. 54 miles
17. 16 mph
18. 7 mph
19. 1 mile
20. 14 miles

Once you are satisfied with your answers, move on to the next practice exam.

PRACTICE TEST 14

There are 20 questions and you have 5 minutes to complete the test. The answers are supplied at the end of the test.

Q1. What speed covers 9 miles in 1 hour and 48 mins?

ANSWER:

Q2. At 90 mph, how far do you travel in 30 mins?

ANSWER:

Q3. At 60 mph, how long does it take to travel 36 miles?

ANSWER:

Q4. At 15 mph, how long does it take to travel 90 miles?

ANSWER:

Q5. At 40 mph, how long does it take to travel 4 miles?

ANSWER:

Q6. At 1 mph, how far do you travel in 6 hours?

ANSWER:

Q7. At 28 mph, how long does it take to travel 21 miles?

ANSWER:

Q8. What speed covers 16 miles in 8 mins?

ANSWER:

Q9. At 19 mph, how long does it take to travel 76 miles?

ANSWER:

Q10. What speed covers 12 miles in 45 mins?

ANSWER:

Q11. At 18 mph, how far do you travel in 40 mins?

ANSWER:

Q12. At 6 mph, how long does it take to travel 14 miles?

ANSWER:

Q13. At 2 mph, how far do you travel in 4 hours?

ANSWER:

Q14. At 32 mph, how long does it take to travel 16 miles?

ANSWER:

Q15. What speed covers 40 miles in 25 mins?

ANSWER:

Q16. What speed covers 33 miles in 3 hours?

ANSWER:

Q17. What speed covers 9 miles in 2 hours and 15 mins?

ANSWER:

Q18. What speed covers 19 miles in 30 mins?

ANSWER:

Q19. What speed covers 6 miles in 9 mins?

ANSWER:

Q20. At 18 mph, how long does it take to travel 12 miles?

ANSWER:

Now check your answers with the ones that follow.

ANSWERS TO PRACTICE TEST 14

1. 5 mph
2. 45 miles
3. 36 mins
4. 6 hours
5. 6 mins
6. 6 miles
7. 45 mins
8. 120 mph
9. 4 hours
10. 16 mph
11. 12 miles
12. 2 hours and 20 mins
13. 8 miles
14. 30 mins
15. 96 mph
16. 11 mph
17. 4 mph
18. 38 mph
19. 40 mph
20. 40 mins

Once you are satisfied with your answers, move on to the next practice exam.

PRACTICE TEST 15

There are 20 questions and you have 5 minutes to complete the test. The answers are supplied at the end of the test.

Q1. What speed covers 210 miles in 3 hours and 45 mins?

ANSWER:

Q2. At 30 mph, how far do you travel in 1 hour and 12 mins?

ANSWER:

Q3. What speed covers 90 miles in 50 mins?

ANSWER:

Q4. At 192 mph, how long does it take to travel 176 miles?

ANSWER:

Q5. At 95 mph, how long does it take to travel 95 miles?

ANSWER:

Q6. At 60 mph, how far do you travel in 12 mins?

ANSWER:

Q7. At 20 mph, how far do you travel in 9 mins?

ANSWER:

Q8. At 3 mph, how long does it take to travel 48 miles?

ANSWER:

Q9. What speed covers 34 miles in 51 mins?

ANSWER:

Q10. At 11 mph, how far do you travel in 1 hour?

ANSWER:

Q11. At 8 mph, how long does it take to travel 22 miles?

ANSWER:

Q12. At 120 mph, how far do you travel in 1 hour and 15 mins?

ANSWER:

Q13. At 6 mph, how long does it take to travel 70 miles?

ANSWER:

Q14. What speed covers 3 miles in 9 mins?

ANSWER:

Q15. What speed covers 18 miles in 18 mins?

ANSWER:

Q16. At 150 mph, how long does it take to travel 20 miles?

ANSWER:

Q17. At 17 mph, how far do you travel in 1 hour?

ANSWER:

Q18. What speed covers 6 miles in 40 mins?

ANSWER:

Q19. At 9 mph, how far do you travel in 2 hours?

ANSWER:

Q20. At 12 mph, how long does it take to travel 16 miles?

ANSWER:

Now check your answers with the ones that follow.

ANSWERS TO PRACTICE TEST 15

1. 56 mph

2. 36 miles

3. 108 mph

4. 55 mins

5. 1 hour

6. 12 miles

7. 3 miles

8. 16 hours

9. 40 mph

10. 11 miles

11. 2 hours and 45 mins

12. 150 miles

13. 11 hours and 40 mins

14. 20 mph

15. 60 mph

16. 8 mins

17. 17 miles

18. 9 mph

19. 18 miles

20. 1 hour and 20 mins

Once you are satisfied with your answers, move on to the next practice exam.

PRACTICE TEST 16

There are 20 questions and you have 5 minutes to complete the test. The answers are supplied at the end of the test.

Q1. At 15 mph, how far do you travel in 12 mins?

ANSWER:

Q2. What speed covers 195 miles in 1 hour?

ANSWER:

Q3. At 14 mph, how long does it take to travel 14 miles?

ANSWER:

Q4. At 400 mph, how long does it take to travel 60 miles?

ANSWER:

Q5. At 260 mph, how far do you travel in 24 mins?

ANSWER:

Q6. At 70 mph, how far do you travel in 36 mins?

ANSWER:

Q7. At 13 mph, how long does it take to travel 26 miles?

ANSWER:

Q8. At 30 mph, how far do you travel in 1 hour and 10 mins?

ANSWER:

Q9. At 5 mph, how far do you travel in 10 hours?

ANSWER:

Q10. At 19 mph, how long does it take to travel 38 miles?

ANSWER:

Q11. At 2 mph, how far do you travel in 30 mins?

ANSWER:

Q12. At 14 mph, how far do you travel in 30 mins?

ANSWER:

Q13. What speed covers 108 miles in 2 hours and 24 mins?

ANSWER:

Q14. At 80 mph, how far do you travel in 30 mins?

ANSWER:

Q15. At 6 mph, how far do you travel in 25 hours?

ANSWER:

Q16. At 30 mph, how far do you travel in 13 hours and 20 mins?

ANSWER:

Q17. What speed covers 51 miles in 34 mins?

ANSWER:

Q18. At 200 mph, how long does it take to travel 60 miles?

ANSWER:

Q19. At 40 mph, how far do you travel in 21 mins?

ANSWER:

Q20. At 19 mph, how long does it take to travel 209 miles?

ANSWER:

Now check your answers with the ones that follow.

ANSWERS TO PRACTICE TEST 16

1. 3 miles
2. 195 mph
3. 1 hour
4. 9 mins
5. 104 miles
6. 42 miles
7. 2 hours
8. 35 miles
9. 50 miles
10. 2 hours
11. 1 mile
12. 7 miles
13. 45 mph
14. 40 miles
15. 150 miles
16. 400 miles
17. 90 mph
18. 18 mins
19. 14 miles
20. 11 hours

Once you are satisfied with your answers, move on to the next practice exam.

PRACTICE TEST 17

There are 20 questions and you have 5 minutes to complete the test. The answers are supplied at the end of the test.

Q1. At 9 mph, how long does it take to travel 18 miles?

ANSWER:

Q2. What speed covers 13 miles in 1 hour?

ANSWER:

Q3. At 3 mph, how far do you travel in 5 hours?

ANSWER:

Q4. At 18 mph, how long does it take to travel 33 miles?

ANSWER:

Q5. At 5 mph, how long does it take to travel 19 miles?

ANSWER:

Q6. At 3 mph, how long does it take to travel 7 miles?

ANSWER:

Q7. At 15 mph, how long does it take to travel 275 miles?

ANSWER:

Q8. At 192 mph, how long does it take to travel 160 miles?

ANSWER:

Q9. At 8 mph, how long does it take to travel 76 miles?

ANSWER:

Q10. What speed covers 4 miles in 30 mins?

ANSWER:

Q11. What speed covers 85 miles in 2 hours and 30 mins?

ANSWER:

Q12. At 4 mph, how long does it take to travel 20 miles?

ANSWER:

Q13. What speed covers 18 miles in 12 mins?

ANSWER:

Q14. What speed covers 28 miles in 24 mins?

ANSWER:

Q15. What speed covers 20 miles in 30 mins?

ANSWER:

Q16. At 22 mph, how far do you travel in 7 hours and 30 mins?

ANSWER:

Q17. What speed covers 285 miles in 5 hours?

ANSWER:

Q18. At 14 mph, how long does it take to travel 280 miles?

ANSWER:

Q19. At 140 mph, how far do you travel in 30 mins?

ANSWER:

Q20. What speed covers 7 miles in 30 mins?

ANSWER:

Now check your answers with the ones that follow.

ANSWERS TO PRACTICE TEST 17

1. 2 hours
2. 13 mph
3. 15 miles
4. 1 hour and 50 mins
5. 3 hours and 48 mins
6. 2 hours and 20 mins
7. 18 hours and 20 mins
8. 50 mins
9. 9 hours and 30 mins
10. 8 mph
11. 34 mph
12. 5 hours
13. 90 mph
14. 70 mph
15. 40 mph
16. 165 miles
17. 57 mph
18. 20 hours
19. 70 miles
20. 14 mph

Once you are satisfied with your answers, move on to the next practice exam.

PRACTICE TEST 18

There are 20 questions and you have 5 minutes to complete the test. The answers are supplied at the end of the test.

Q1. At 60 mph, how long does it take to travel 12 miles?

ANSWER:

Q2. At 1 mph, how long does it take to travel 12 miles?

ANSWER:

Q3. At 3 mph, how long does it take to travel 10 miles?

ANSWER:

Q4. What speed covers 9 miles in 1 hour and 30 mins?

ANSWER:

Q5. What speed covers 56 miles in 2 hours and 48 mins?

ANSWER:

Q6. At 4 mph, how long does it take to travel 16 miles?

ANSWER:

Q7. What speed covers 15 miles in 9 mins?

ANSWER:

Q8. At 42 mph, how long does it take to travel 14 miles?

ANSWER:

Q9. At 15 mph, how long does it take to travel 120 miles?

ANSWER:

Q10. At 15 mph, how long does it take to travel 2 miles?

ANSWER:

Q11. At 19 mph, how long does it take to travel 76 miles?

ANSWER:

Q12. At 20 mph, how long does it take to travel 11 miles?

ANSWER:

Q13. At 120 mph, how far do you travel in 22 mins?

ANSWER:

Q14. At 3 mph, how far do you travel in 2 hours and 20 mins?

ANSWER:

Q15. At 1 mph, how long does it take to travel 1 mile?

ANSWER:

Q16. At 12 mph, how far do you travel in 30 mins?

ANSWER:

Q17. At 30 mph, how far do you travel in 30 minutes?

ANSWER:

Q18. At 100 mph, how long does it take to travel 180 miles?

ANSWER:

Q19. At 72 mph, how far do you travel in 1 hour and 5 mins?

ANSWER:

Q20. At 54 mph, how long does it take to travel 9 miles?

ANSWER:

Now check your answers with the ones that follow.

ANSWERS TO PRACTICE TEST 18

1. 12 mins
2. 12 hours
3. 3 hours and 20 mins
4. 6 mph
5. 20 mph
6. 4 hours
7. 100 mph
8. 20 mins
9. 8 hours
10. 8 mins
11. 4 hours
12. 33 mins
13. 44 miles
14. 7 miles
15. 1 hour
16. 6 miles
17. 15 miles
18. 1 hour and 48 mins
19. 78 miles
20. 10 mins

Once you are satisfied with your answers, move on to the next practice exam.

PRACTICE TEST 19

There are 20 questions and you have 5 minutes to complete the test. The answers are supplied at the end of the test.

Q1. A man is walking along the street at 7 ft/sec. How far will he walk in 57 secs?

ANSWER:

Q2. A train is moving at 40 km/hrs. How far will it travel in 6 hr?

ANSWER:

Q3. A man is walking along the street at 3 m/sec. How far will he walk in 53 secs?

ANSWER:

Q4. A deer is running across an open field at 5 m/sec. How far will the deer run in 25 secs?

ANSWER:

Q5. A dog runs 3 m/sec. How far will the dog run in 42 secs?

ANSWER:

Q6. A bus is moving along the road at 11 miles per hour. How far will it travel in 7 hrs?

ANSWER:

Q7. An insect is crawling in a straight line at a speed of 3 cm/sec. How far will this insect move in 54 secs?

ANSWER:

Q8. Jim travels 45 miles at 15 mph. How long does it take him?

ANSWER:

 THE **TESTING** SERIES

Q9. Janet walks at 4 mph for 2½ hours. How far does she walk?

ANSWER:

Q10. Margaret drives at a constant speed. In the first three hours she travels 81 miles. How far will she have travelled after 5 hours?

ANSWER:

Q11. Calculate the distance that you would travel if you drove for 3 hours at 20 mph.

ANSWER:

Q12. Calculate the distance that you would travel if you drove for 8 hours at 60 mph.

ANSWER:

Q13. Calculate the distance that you would travel if you drove for half an hour at 76 mph.

ANSWER:

Q14. Calculate the distance that you would travel if you drove for 1½ hours at 42 mph.

ANSWER:

Q15. How long does it take to travel 120 miles at 40 mph?

ANSWER:

Q16. How long does it take to travel 300 miles at 50 mph?

ANSWER:

Q17. How long does it take to travel 240 miles at 60 mph?

ANSWER:

Q18. How long does it take to travel 385 miles at 70 mph?

ANSWER:

Q19. A car travels 300 miles in 5 hours. What is the average speed of the car?

ANSWER:

Q20. Jim can row at an average speed of 2 metres per second. How long does it take him to row 70m?

ANSWER:

Now check your answers with the ones that follow.

ANSWERS TO PRACTICE TEST 19

1. 399 ft
2. 240 km
3. 159 m
4. 125 m
5. 126 m
6. 77 miles
7. 162 cm
8. 3 hours
9. 10 miles
10. 135 miles
11. 60 miles
12. 480 miles
13. 38 miles
14. 63 miles
15. 3 hours
16. 6 hours
17. 4 hours
18. 5 hours and 30 mins
19. 60 miles per hour
20. 35 seconds

Once you are satisfied with your answers, move on to the next practice exam.

PRACTICE TEST 20

There are 20 questions and you have 5 minutes to complete the test. The answers are supplied at the end of the test.

Q1. At 84 mph, how long does it take to travel 112 miles?

ANSWER:

Q2. At 12 mph, how far do you travel in 7 hours and 30 mins?

ANSWER:

Q3. At 9 mph, how long does it take to travel 18 miles?

ANSWER:

Q4. At 10 mph, how far do you travel in 18 mins?

ANSWER:

Q5. At 14 mph, how far do you travel in 30 mins?

ANSWER:

Q6. What speed covers 60 miles in 1 hour and 40 mins?

ANSWER:

Q7. At 15 mph, how long does it take to travel 20 miles?

ANSWER:

Q8. At 4 mph, how far do you travel in 20 hours?

ANSWER:

Q9. At 34 mph, how far do you travel in 10 hours?

ANSWER:

Q10. What speed covers 6 miles in 15 mins?

ANSWER:

Q11. At 5 mph, how long does it take to travel 4 miles?

ANSWER:

Q12. What speed covers 12 miles in 45 mins?

ANSWER:

Q13. What speed covers 11 miles in 20 mins?

ANSWER:

Q14. What speed covers 33 miles in 1 hour and 30 mins?

ANSWER:

Q15. At 18 mph, how long does it take to travel 42 miles?

ANSWER:

Q16. What speed covers 17 miles in 15 mins?

ANSWER:

Q17. At 85 mph, how long does it take to travel 204 miles?

ANSWER:

Q18. What speed covers 14 miles in 4 hours and 40 mins?

ANSWER:

Q19. What speed covers 13 miles in 1 hour?

ANSWER:

Q20. At 16 mph, how far do you travel in 3 hours?

ANSWER:

Now check your answers with the ones that follow.

ANSWERS TO PRACTICE TEST 20

1. 1 hour and 20 mins
2. 90 miles
3. 2 hours
4. 3 miles
5. 7 miles
6. 36 mph
7. 1 hour and 20 mins
8. 80 miles
9. 340 miles
10. 24 mph
11. 48 mins
12. 16 mph
13. 33 mph
14. 22 mph
15. 2 hours and 20 mins
16. 68 mph
17. 2 hours and 24 mins
18. 3 mph
19. 13 mph
20. 48 miles

CHAPTER 4
MOCK EXAM 1

During this mock exam, you have 60 minutes to answer all of the questions. For this test, calculators are PERMITTED. We understand that the majority of SDT tests do not allow you to use a calculator, but in order to gain a more advanced understanding, we have provided you with harder questions, so that you can fully utilise your skills.

(Give all answers to the nearest whole number).

Q1. You are travelling at 28 mph for 75 minutes. How far do you travel?

ANSWER:

Q2. You travel 15 miles in half an hour. What speed are you travelling at?

ANSWER:

Q3. You travel 33 miles at a constant speed of 55 mph. How long are you travelling for?

ANSWER:

Q4. You are travelling at 75 mph for 1 hour and 20 minutes. How far do you travel?

ANSWER:

Q5. You travel 61 miles in 1 hour and 1 minute. What speed are you travelling at?

ANSWER:

Q6. You travel 90 miles at a constant speed of 30 mph. How long are you travelling for?

ANSWER:

Q7. You are travelling at 70 mph for 150 minutes. How far do you travel?

ANSWER:

Q8. You travel 2.5 miles in 5 minutes. What speed are you travelling at?

ANSWER:

Q9. You travel 75 miles at a constant speed of 45 mph. How long are you travelling for?

ANSWER:

Q10. You are travelling at 59 mph for quarter of an hour. How far do you travel?

ANSWER:

Q11. You travel 325 miles in 4 hours and 10 minutes. What speed are you travelling at?

ANSWER:

Q12. You travel 38 miles at 45 mph. How long are you travelling for?

ANSWER:

Q13. You are travelling at 80 mph for 15 minutes. How far do you travel?

ANSWER:

Q14. You travel 63 miles in 45 minutes. What speed are you travelling at?

ANSWER:

Q15. You travel 18 miles at 50 mph. How long are you travelling for?

ANSWER:

Q16. You are travelling at 65 mph for 1 hour and 10 minutes. How far do you travel?

ANSWER:

Q17. You travel 120 miles in 2 hours. What speed are you travelling at?

ANSWER:

Q18. You travel 80 miles at 50 mph. How long are you travelling for?

ANSWER:

Q19. You are travelling at 40 mph for half an hour. How far do you travel?

ANSWER:

Q20. You travel 80 miles in 1 ¾ of an hour. What speed are you travelling at?

ANSWER:

Q21. You travel 35 miles at 70 mph. How long are you travelling for?

ANSWER:

Q22. You are travelling at 15 mph for 8 minutes. How far do you travel?

ANSWER:

Q23. You travel 16 miles in quarter of an hour. What speed are you travelling at?

ANSWER:

Q24. You travel 60 miles at 50 mph. How long are you travelling for?

ANSWER:

Q25. You are travelling at 30 mph for 10 minutes. How far do you travel?

ANSWER:

Q26. You travel 75 miles in one and half hours. What speed are you travelling at?

ANSWER:

Q27. You travel 1 mile at 60 mph. How long are you travelling for?

ANSWER:

Q28. You are travelling at 50 mph for 2 and half hours. How far do you travel?

ANSWER:

Q29. You travel 100 miles in 1 hour and 15 minutes. What speed are you travelling at?

ANSWER:

Q30. You travel 600 miles at 80 mph. How long are you travelling for?

ANSWER:

Q31. If you travel at 100 mph for 2 and half hours, what distance will you cover?

ANSWER:

Q32. You are travelling at 56 mph for 1 hour. How far do you travel?

ANSWER:

Q33. You travel 10 miles in 20 minutes. You then stop for a 5 minute break. You then continue on your journey for a further 20 minutes which covers another 15 miles. What is your average speed?

ANSWER:

Q34. You travel 30 miles at a constant speed of 60 mph. You get stuck in traffic for 15 minutes. When you continue your journey, you travel at 45 mph for another 12 miles. How long does your journey take you?

ANSWER:

Q35. If you travel at 85 mph for 1 hour, what distance will you cover?

ANSWER:

Q36. You leave base at 1023. You arrive at your destination at 1113. You travel 31 miles. What is your speed?

ANSWER:

Q37. You fly towards Target at 138 mph. You need 1 minute to hit the target. The total distance you cover is 14 miles. What is the duration of your task?

ANSWER:

Q38. You leave base at 1321. You arrive at target A at 1330. You hit target A which takes 1 minute. It takes 6 minutes to reach target B. Again, it takes 1 minute to hit target B. It takes 9 minutes to return to base. You travel at an average speed of 190 mph. What distance do you cover?

ANSWER:

Q39. Work is 28 miles from home. You travel at 60 mph for the first quarter of the journey. The remaining journey you travel at 70 mph. What time did you leave home if you arrive at work at 0903?

ANSWER:

Q40. You travel 75 miles at a speed of 70 mph. You stay at your destination for 1 ¾ hours. You then return, travelling at a speed of 80 mph. How long are you away from home?

ANSWER:

Q41. You need to arrive at a destination at 1315. You are 23 miles away. Your friend, who lives 10 miles away calls you and asks you to wait for them at their house for five minutes so they can ride with you. The route has a speed limit of 50 mph. What time do you need to leave?

ANSWER:

Q42. If you are travelling a distance of 150 miles and aim to complete the journey in exactly two hours including a 15 minute rest break, what speed do you need to travel at?

ANSWER:

Q43. You need to arrive at a destination within 5 minutes, you are 8 miles away and it will take you 1 minute to prepare the jet. What speed do you need to travel at?

ANSWER:

Q44. You fly at 200 mph, for 180 miles. How long are you flying for?

ANSWER:

Q45. You have half an hour to reach your target, hit it & return. The target is 48 miles away. What speed do you need to fly at?

ANSWER:

Q46. When you reach your destination, you will have covered a total of 320 miles, flying at 195 mph. You had to stop half way through the journey to refuel which took quarter of an hour. What is your total flying time?

ANSWER:

Q47. At 1500, you receive a task to pick up cargo that is 105 miles away. You need to be there and back within the hour. Once you have the cargo, you can travel at a maximum of 175 mph. What speed do you need to travel there at?

ANSWER:

Q48. You are carrying cargo which forces you to drive at a maximum of 70 mph. You have to drive the cargo 80 miles. How long will this take you?

ANSWER:

Q49. On Monday mornings, it is your duty to ensure all vehicles are fuelled and clean. There are 5 stops; you spend 20 minutes at each. Each stop is 5 miles apart. The first stop is 23 miles away. You travel at a constant speed of 70 mph.

a. What time will you finish at the first stop if you leave at 0630.

b. Assuming you did not stop at any of the stops and left your house at 0630, what distance would you have travelled by 0718?

ANSWER A:

ANSWER B:

50. Work out what time you left, if you arrive at your destination at 1703 and covered 54 miles, travelling at 65 mph.

ANSWER:

For the following questions, the jet's speed will be in knots. Please answer any speed questions in knots, to the nearest whole number.
(1 knot = 1.15 mph)

Q51. Work out the total distance covered if you are travelling at 202 knots for ¾ hour.

ANSWER:

Q52. You leave base at 1206. You arrive at your destination at 1213. You travel 24 miles. What is your speed? In knots.

ANSWER:

Q53. You fly towards a target at 138 knots. The total distance you cover is 31 miles. What is the duration of your task?

ANSWER:

Q54. You leave your base at 0702. You are two minutes late. You are supposed to arrive at 0930. You need to cover 55 miles.

a. What speed would you have travelled at if you left on time?

b. What speed will you need to travel at to get to your destination at 09:00?

ANSWER A:

ANSWER B:

Q55. You fly for 1 ½ hours at 189 knots. What distance do you cover?

ANSWER:

Q56. You leave your house at 1005. You travel for half an hour at 50 mph. When you reach the motorway, the traffic forces you to drive at 15 mph for 12 minutes. After the traffic clears, you continue your journey at 50 mph and arrive at your destination at 1125.

a. How far do you travel in total?

b. How long does the third part of your journey take you?

c. How long would you have been travelling for if you had not got stuck in traffic, assuming you remained at 50 mph the whole journey?

ANSWER A:

ANSWER B:

ANSWER C:

Q57. You are travelling from 0942 to 1158. You travel 190.4 miles. What speed are you travelling at?

ANSWER:

Q58. There are two parts to your journey: for the first part you travel 87 miles at a constant speed of 70 mph. You have a rest at the services for quarter of an hour at 1321. You finish the second part of your journey at 1453, travelling a total of 93 miles.

a. How long does the first part of your journey take?

b. What is the total duration of your journey?

c. What speed do you travel at for the second part of your journey?

ANSWER A:

ANSWER B:

ANSWER C:

Q59. You leave your house at 0824. Your journey to work is 21 miles. You usually arrive at 0855. Today, there is slow moving traffic and you are forced to drive at an average speed of 27 mph.

a. What speed do you usually travel to work at?

b. What time will you arrive at work today?

ANSWER A:

ANSWER B:

Q60. You left work at 1703. You arrived home at 1756. You sat in standstill traffic for 21 minutes. You travelled a total of 19 miles. What is your average moving speed? (i.e. excluding anytime you are not moving).

ANSWER:

Q61. At 0822, you and your friend embark on a road trip. You take turns in driving. You drive 130 miles at a speed of 65 mph. You have a pit stop at a service station, and return to the road at 1051. Your friend then drives for 4 hours on cruise control at a speed of 75 mph. You pull into a petrol station and it takes 10 minutes to fill up. You continue for the remaining 165 miles. You arrive at your destination for the night at 1818.

a. How long does the first stage of the journey take, before the pit stop?

b. How many miles does your friend cover?

c. What speed do you drive at the last part of your journey?

d. What is the total distance covered?

e. Who drives for the longest amount of time?

f. Who drives the most miles?

ANSWER A:

ANSWER B:

ANSWER C:

ANSWER D:

ANSWER E:

ANSWER F:

Q62. The distance between yours and Michelle's house is 8 miles. The distance between yours and Ryan's house is 6 miles. Michelle and Ryan live 5 miles apart. You leave your house at 1823 and drive at 40 mph. You then leave Michelle's house at 2003 and arrive at Ryan's house at 2010.

a. What time do you arrive at Michelle's?

b. At what speed do you travel to Ryan's at?

c. What is your total time travelling?

ANSWER A:

ANSWER B:

ANSWER C:

Q63. Your job is 56 miles away. You plan to leave at 0830. You have to be there at 0930.

a. What speed will you need to travel at in order to be there on time?

b. If you wanted to drive at 30 mph, what time would you need to leave?

ANSWER A:

ANSWER B:

Q64. You travel 6 miles and it takes you 6 minutes. You get a flat tire and have to wait 23 minutes for the rescue van to arrive. The van tows you home, which is 20 miles away. He is only travelling 25 mph.

a. At what speed are you travelling before you get the flat tire?

b. How long are you out in total?

ANSWER A:

ANSWER B:

Q65. You are flying to a battle station and receive a call that you need to visit two stop stations in the next half an hour. One station is 23 miles away and the other is 36 miles away. You will be at each stop station for 2 minutes. How fast do you need to travel in order to complete the task?

ANSWER:

Q66. At 0654, you receive a command to fly north for 85 miles. The commander needs you to be in position at 0715. What speed do you need to travel at?

ANSWER:

Q67. You are travelling for 25 minutes. Your speed is 155 mph. You stop for refueling which takes 3 minutes. You then continue with your journey. You cover a total of 119 miles in ¾ hour.

a. How far do you travel before refueling?

b. At what speed do you travel for the second part of your journey?

ANSWER A:

ANSWER B:

Q68. You need to get to and hit target B within 3 minutes after hitting target A. Target B and A are equal distances from the base. The total distance from base, to both targets then returning to base is 192 miles. You leave at 1103. You hit target B at 1125 travelling 200 mph. You return to base travelling at 195 mph.

a. What speed do you travel from base to target A?

b. What is the distance between target A and B?

c. What time do you return to base?

ANSWER A: [ ]

ANSWER B: [ ]

ANSWER C: [ ]

ANSWERS TO MOCK EXAM 1

1. 35 miles
2. 30 mph
3. 36 mins
4. 100 miles
5. 60 mph
6. 3 hours
7. 175 miles
8. 30 mph
9. 1 hour 40 minutes
10. 15 miles
11. 78 mph
12. 51 mins
13. 20 miles
14. 84 mph
15. 22 minutes
16. 76 miles
17. 60 mph
18. 1 hour 36 mins
19. 20 miles
20. 46 mph
21. 30 mins
22. 2 miles
23. 64 mph
24. 1 hour 12 mins
25. 5 miles
26. 50 mph
27. 1 minute
28. 125 miles
29. 80 mph
30. 7 hours 30 minutes
31. 250 miles
32. 56 miles
33. 38 mph
34. 1 hr 1 min
35. 85 miles
36. 37 mph
37. 7 minutes
38. 82 miles
39. 0838
40. 3hrs 45mins
41. 1242
42. 86 mph
43. 120 mph
44. 54 mins
45. 192 mph
46. 1 hr and 53 mins
47. 263 mph
48. 1hr 9mins
49. a) 0710
49. b) 56 miles
50. 1613
51. 174 miles
52. 179knots
53. 12 minutes
54. a) 22 mph
54. b) 28 mph
55. 326miles
56. a) 60 miles
56. b) 38 minutes
56. c) 1 hr 12 mins
57. 84 mph
58. a) 1 hr 15 mins
58. b) 2 hrs 47 mins
58. c) 72 mph
59. a) 41 mph
59. b) 0911
60. 36mph
61. a) 2hrs
61. b) 300 miles
61. c) 50 mph
61. d) 595 miles
61. e) you
61. f) your friend
62. a) 1835
62. b) 43 mph
62. c) 19 mins
63. a) 56 mph
63. b) 0738
64. a) 60 mph
64. b) 1hr 17 mins
65. 136 mph
66. 243 mph
67. a) 65 miles
67. b) 159 mph
68. a) 287 mph
68. b) 10miles
68. c) 1158

CHAPTER 5
MOCK EXAM 2

During this mock exam, you have 60 minutes to answer the questions. For this test, you are NOT permitted to use a calculator.

(Give all answers to the nearest whole number).

Q1. You are going to drive to your friend's house. She lives 17 miles away from you with an average speed limit of 30 mph. Your friend asks for an estimated time of arrival. If you leave your house at 1415, and you stick to the speed limit, what time will you arrive at your friend's house? (Assuming there is no traffic).

ANSWER:

Q2. You are travelling at 22 mph for 30 minutes. How far would you have travelled?

ANSWER:

Q3. You travel 80 miles at a constant speed of 20 mph. How long are you travelling for?

ANSWER:

Q4. You are travelling 110 miles at an average speed of 60 mph. How long are you travelling for?

ANSWER:

Q5. You travel 12 miles in ¾ of an hour. What speed are you travelling?

ANSWER:

Q6. You travel for 3 hours at a speed of 70 mph. What is the distance you have travelled?

ANSWER:

Q7. What speed covers 42 miles in 3 hours?

ANSWER:

Q8. How far do you travel in 12 minutes, if you are travelling at the speed of 10 mph?

ANSWER:

Q9. How far do you travel in 7 hours, if you are travelling at the speed of 30 mph?

ANSWER:

Q10. What speed covers 2 miles in 16 minutes?

ANSWER:

Q11. How long would it take you to travel 10 miles at 5 mph?

ANSWER:

Q12. What speed will you be driving if you completed 15 miles in 10 minutes?

ANSWER:

Q13. How long will you be travelling for if you travel 118 miles at a rate of 60 mph?

ANSWER:

Q14. You travel 5 miles in 10 minutes. What speed are you travelling at?

ANSWER:

Q15. You travel at a rate of 15 mph for 2 hours. What is the distance you will be travelling?

ANSWER:

Q16. What speed are you travelling if you drive 72 miles in 1 hour and 30 minutes?

ANSWER:

Q17. What speed would you need to travel at if you wanted to complete 25 miles in 10 minutes?

ANSWER:

Q18. If you travel 0.5 miles in 30 seconds, what speed are you travelling at?

ANSWER:

Q19. You travel 20 miles at an average speed of 80 mph. How long are you travelling for?

ANSWER:

Q20. What rate of speed are you travelling at if you travel 60 miles in 30 minutes?

ANSWER:

Q21. How long would it take you to travel 80 miles at 40 mph?

ANSWER:

Q22. How far would you travel if you travelled at 50 mph for 30 minutes?

ANSWER:

Q23. What rate of speed are you travelling at if you travel 45 miles in 5 hours?

ANSWER:

Q24. You travel 22 miles in 30 minutes. What speed are you travelling at?

ANSWER:

Q25. You travel 25 miles in 3 minutes. What speed are you travelling at?

ANSWER:

Q26. You travel 30 miles at 50 mph. How long are you travelling for?

ANSWER:

Q27. You travel at a rate of 40 mph for 1 hour and 15 minutes. How far do you travel?

ANSWER:

Q28. You travel 60 miles in 1 ¼ of an hour. What speed are you travelling at?

ANSWER:

Q29. How far would you travel at 4 mph for 1 hour?

ANSWER:

Q30. You leave work at 1805. You arrive home at 1855. You travel 20 miles. What average speed is your journey home?

ANSWER:

Q31. You need to transport an ice sculpture in the back of your van. You need to transport it 18 miles, at a rate of 10 mph. How long will this take you?

ANSWER:

Q32. You fly at 200 mph for 80 miles. How long are you flying for?

ANSWER:

Q33. You travel for 3 hours at the speed of approximately 50 mph. How many miles do you travel?

ANSWER:

Q34. You drive at 22 mph for 4 hours. What distance do you travel?

ANSWER:

Q35. You decide to take a midnight drive. You leave your house at 23.55 and arrive back at 01.25. You drove at a speed of 30 mph. How many miles did your journey consist of?

ANSWER:

Q36. How long will it take you to travel 100 miles at a rate of 25 mph?

ANSWER:

Q37. Joe, David and Dan take it in turns driving from London to Dover, a total distance of approximately 80 miles per driver. Joe drives for 1 hour, David drives for 1 hour and 20 minutes, and Dan drives for 1 hour and 15 minutes.

a. Calculate the average speed for Joe.

b. Calculate the average speed for David.

c. Calculate the average speed for Dan.

ANSWER A:

ANSWER B:

ANSWER C:

Q38. How long will it take you to travel 180 miles at a rate of 60 mph?

ANSWER:

Q39. How many miles would you travel at 50 mph for 30 mins?

ANSWER:

Q40. Emma can type 50 words in 1 minute. Calculate her typing speed in:

a. Words per 30 seconds;

b. Words per half an hour;

c. Words every 2 hours.

ANSWER A:

ANSWER B:

ANSWER C:

Q41. Scarlett walks at 3mph for 3 hours and 40 minutes. If she continues to walk at this constant speed, how far would Scarlett have walked in 7 hours and 20 minutes?

ANSWER:

Q42. What speed would you be travelling at if you were to complete 400 miles in 5 hours?

ANSWER:

Q43. Gareth has to travel 200 miles. He travels the first 100 miles in 2 hours.

a. What is Gareth's average speed for the first part of his journey?

b. If Gareth's speed remains the same throughout the journey, how long will it take him to complete the whole journey?

ANSWER A:

ANSWER B:

Q44. A slug moves 10 metres in 4 hours.

a. Calculate how many metres the slug will move in 12 hours.

b. Calculate the distance, in metres, the slug moves in 1 hour.

c. Calculate the time it takes the slug to move 5 metres.

ANSWER A:

ANSWER B:

ANSWER C:

Q45. What speed would you be travelling at if you were to complete 60 miles in 20 minutes?

ANSWER:

Q46. What speed covers 750 miles in 2 hours?

ANSWER:

Q47. At 340 mph, how far do you travel in 3 hours?

ANSWER:

Q48. A train is moving at a rate of 50km/h. How far will it travel in 3 hours?

ANSWER:

Q49. What is the average speed of a car if it travels 40 miles in 25 minutes?

ANSWER:

Q50. You travel 400 miles in 8 hours. What speed are you travelling at?

ANSWER:

Q51. You have travelled 40 miles at an average speed of 50 mph. You get stuck in traffic for 35 minutes. When the traffic clears, you continue your journey at a speed of 40 mph for another 20 miles. How long does your entire journey take?

ANSWER:

Q52. You travel 150 miles in 1 hour and 30 minutes. What speed are you travelling at?

ANSWER:

Q53. You travel a total of 500 miles in 4 hours. What speed are you travelling at?

ANSWER:

Q54. How long will it take you to get home if you left work at 1608 and covered 45 miles, travelling at 30 mph.

ANSWER:

Q55. You leave home at 0945. You arrive at your destination at 1120. You travel 76 miles. What is your average speed?

ANSWER:

Q56. You are travelling a total distance of 180 miles and hope to complete the journey in 4 hours. What speed will you need to travel at if you wish to stick to this time frame?

ANSWER:

Q57. Katie and Harrison take a road trip. There are two parts of the journey in which they decide to split the driving. For the first part of the journey, Katie travels 90 miles at an average speed of 60 mph. They stop off at a petrol station for 20 minutes, before Harrison takes over the next part of the driving. They leave the petrol station at 1355 and arrive at their destination at 1525, travelling a distance of 60 miles.

a. What is the duration of the whole journey?

b. How long does the first part of the journey take?

c. What speed do you travel at for the second part of the journey?

ANSWER A:

ANSWER B:

ANSWER C:

Q58. You are starting a new job and are trying to work out how long it will take you to get to work. Your job is 44 miles away, and you need to be there by 0845.

a) What speed will you need to travel at, if you leave your house at 0750?

b) If you wanted to drive at an average speed of 40 mph, what time would you need to leave your house in order to get to work on time?

ANSWER A:

ANSWER A:

Q59. You travel at an average speed of 62 mph for 124 miles. You arrive at your destination, and spend 4 hours there before heading home. For your return journey, you travel at 40 mph.

a) How long were you away from home in total?

b) How long was your return journey?

c) How long was the first part of your journey?

ANSWER A:

ANSWER B:

ANSWER C:

Q60. You travel 24 miles in 30 minutes. What speed are you travelling at?

ANSWER:

Q61. If you travel 80 miles for 1 hour and 20 minutes, what speed are you travelling at?

ANSWER:

Q62. You are travelling at 56 mph for 75 minutes. How far do you travel?

ANSWER:

Q63. You are travelling at 50 mph for 30 minutes. How far will you travel?

ANSWER:

Q64. If you travel at 95 mph for 1 hour, what distance will you cover?

ANSWER:

Q65. You fly at 200 mph for 120 miles. How long are you flying for?

ANSWER:

Q66. Work out the total distance if you travelled for 2 and a half hours at a speed of 70 mph.

ANSWER:

Q67. What speed will you need to travel at if you wanted to complete 5 miles in 2 and a half minutes?

ANSWER:

Q68. How long will it take you to travel 10 miles at a rate of 2 mph?

ANSWER:

ANSWERS TO MOCK EXAM 2

1. 1449
2. 11 miles
3. 4 hrs
4. 1 hr and 50 mins
5. 16 mph
6. 210 miles
7. 14 mph
8. 2 miles
9. 210 miles
10. 8 mph
11. 2 hrs
12. 90 mph
13. 1 hr and 58 mins
14. 30 mph
15. 30 miles
16. 48 mph
17. 150 mph
18. 60 mph
19. 15 mins
20. 120 mph
21. 2 hrs
22. 25 miles
23. 9 mph
24. 44 mph
25. 500 mph
26. 36 mins
27. 50 miles

28. 48 mph
29. 4 miles
30. 24 mph
31. 1 hr and 48 mins
32. 24 mins
33. 150 miles
34. 88 miles
35. 45 miles
36. 4 hrs
37. a) 80 mph
37. b) 60 mph
37. c) 64 mph
38. 3 hrs
39. 25 miles
40. a) 25
40. b) 1500
40. c) 6000
41. 22 miles
42. 80 mph
43. a) 50 mph
43. b) 4 hrs
44. a) 30 metres
44. b) 2.5 metres
44. c) 2 hours
45. 180 mph
46. 375 mph
47. 1020 miles

48. 150 kilometres
49. 96 mph
50. 50 mph
51. 1 hr and 53 mins
52. 100 mph
53. 125 mph
54. 1 hr and 30 mins
55. 48 mph
56. 45 mph
57. a) 3 hrs and 20 mins
57. b) 1 hr and 30 mins
57. c) 40 mph
58. a) 48 mph
58. b) 0739
59. a) 9 hrs and 6 mins
59. b) 3 hrs and 6 mins
59. c) 2 hrs
60. 48 mph
61. 60 mph
62. 70 miles
63. 25 miles
64. 95 miles
65. 36 mins
66. 175 miles
67. 120 mph
68. 5 hrs

Visit www.how2become.com to find more titles and courses that will help you to pass any job interview or selection process:

- Online Armed forces testing

- Job interview DVDs and books

- 1-day intensive career training courses

- Psychometric testing books and CDs

WWW.HOW2BECOME.COM

 THE **TESTING** SERIES

Printed in Great Britain
by Amazon